A Word from the Publisher

TERRY AND THE PIRATES is the sixth book to be published in *THE GOLDEN AGE OF THE COMICS* series. The entire list consists of the following titles:

1 — LITTLE NEMO IN SLUMBERLAND............................*By Winsor McCay*

2 — FLASH GORDON...*By Alex Raymond*

3 — THE PHANTOM...*By Lee Falk*

4 — KRAZY KAT..*By George Herriman*
(Published in cooperation with Grosset and Dunlap)

5 — LITTLE NEMO IN SLUMBERLAND
(Italian edition — published in cooperation with Garzanti Editore — 112 color plates)

6 — TERRY AND THE PIRATES..*By Milton Caniff*

CURRENTLY IN PREPARATION

7 — MANDRAKE THE MAGICIAN...*By Lee Falk*

8 — PRINCE VALIANT...*By Hal Foster*

9 — MINUTE MOVIES...*By Ed Wheelan*

10 — POPEYE... *By E. Segar*

11 — THE E.C. HORROR COMICS................................*Compiled by Bill Gaines*

12 — FLASH GORDON — The First Adventures....................*By Alex Raymond*

PUBLISHER

© 1970
Chicago Tribune-New York News Syndicate, Inc., and Nostalgia Press, Inc.
Library of Congress catalogue number 70-132469

by

NOSTALGIA PRESS, BOX 293, FRANKLIN SQUARE, N.Y. 11010

EDITED BY MAURICE HORN
Book design by Maurice Horn
Artwork by Ted Moskowitz

We gratefully acknowledge Len Brown, Dave Kaler, Frank
Engli, and Adelaide Gilchrest for their helpful contribution to
this book. We especially wish to thank Milton Caniff for his
invaluable advice, generous assistance, and kind encouragement.

CONTENTS

TERRY, THE PIRATES, AND I
by Milton Caniff

MILTON CANIFF BEFORE TERRY
a portfolio

INTRODUCING: TERRY AND THE PIRATES
by Maurice Horn

FIRST EPISODE:
The Lost Gold Mine

SECOND EPISODE:
On a Mystery Cruise

THIRD EPISODE:
Thieves and Lovers

Terry, the Pirates and I

by

When the editors told me of the plans for this volume I was pleased, but surprised. I was never a collector or buff when I was first attracted to cartooning. Cataloging even my own work was never a preoccupation of mine.

I had certain favorites from whom I cribbed. Others I admired, but was unable to imitate, yet I did not clip and file. When I first had work published I did not even retain cuttings — until it became evident that an active batch of samples was the only means of demonstrating an unknown's talents to an editor or other art buyer.

A retrospective display such as this reveals the often crude results of the pressures of deadlines and the heat of suddenly being published in the country's two largest newspapers, the N. Y. News and the Chicago Tribune.

In 1934 I was drawing DICKIE DARE and THE GAY THIRTIES for the Associated Press. DICKIE had started in the New York POST, then switched to the N. Y. SUN when the POST changed hands.

When Joseph Patterson, publisher of the N. Y. NEWS, invited me to create a new adventure story for his newspaper I was six weeks ahead on DICKIE (daily only) and doing a Sunday color page was an adventure in itself. The N. Y. NEWS Sunday deadline was eight weeks ahead and we were paid on publication. The daily strips were four weeks ahead of publication, with the same financial arrangement.

The A. P. income had stopped and the NEWS not yet begun, so I was in the frustrating position of having cartoon strips running in *two* major New York newspapers while being unable to pay the rent on my apartment. For a long time our entire recreation consisted of miniature golf at ten cents per round.

Rereading these TERRY efforts recalls the on-the-job training which confronted the new cartoonists then. There were no double by-lines. The creator of a feature was expected to write *and* draw. Later, assuming success, the by-liner could hire an assistant (or assistants) and deliver an effective conglomerate, but at the start had no choice but to plow into the problem and grab sleep as a hospital intern learns to do between calls.

I would write the six daily releases on Monday, pencil on Tuesday, ink figures on Wednesday, backgrounds on Thursday, write the Sunday page on Friday, pencil on Saturday, ink on Sunday, then start the cycle again.

A combination diversion and going to school to sample the public temper were the midnight movies then popular in New York.

Current general appeal fiction such as that in the SATURDAY EVENING POST was a further testing ground. Material bought by the editors of the magazines, plus an echoing of the front page news, was the sounding board for most of the story strips of the thirties.

From the start in TERRY the thrust was to grab the reader who thought he led a dull life and longed for the exotic charms of the Orient. When thousands of Americans later made the trip involuntarily, they learned that the DRAGON LADY really existed only in the DAILY NEWS Building in New York.

None of this was meant as a put-on. I was just as caught up in the lure of the far places as anyone else — and I was equally pinioned to a clock. My job was not dull, but it consumed the physically available day. It was not until Noel Sickles, then drawing SCORCHY SMITH, and with whom I shared a studio, worked out a means of delivering illustration quality pictures on a seven-day basis was I able to buck some of the chains of working schedule while dramatically improving the all-over value of TERRY. I shall always be grateful that Noel allowed me to pick his brain those formative years.

Today in STEVE CANYON I continue to use Sickels' formula and it has lost none of its original effectiveness.

I sometimes have nightmares in which I am sentenced to starting with the first TERRY strip and redraw every line up to the current release of STEVE CANYON. Frightening as that prospect is, I shall at this very moment turn to the board and re-enact exactly the same ritual that I have been following since October 1934. There is a blank set of strips and a Sunday page to be completed. The saving difference is that no two daily releases are ever alike — and I can't wait to find out what will happen tomorrow.

Milton Caniff before Terry:

A portfolio

1—
From the Stivers
High School (Dayton)
yearbook, 1925.

2—
"The Gay Thirties", 1934.
(c) AP Newsfeatures.

3, 4—
From the Columbus
Dispatch, 1927.

Wherein Mr. Caniff Protests Against the Angular Ladies of Fashion

1, 2—
"Chic and Noodles",
Caniff's first comic-strip;
from "Stivers News", 1925.

1—
"Life is like that";
from the Columbus
Dispatch, 1928.
2—
Christmas shopping
reminder, 1932.
© AP Newsfeatures.

Three 1932 drawings
showing Milton Caniff's
versatility and wide
imaginative range.
1, 2, 3. © AP Newsfeatures.

"SAVE YA VOICE MAME, WE GOT A MIDNIGHT SHOW."

Humor cartoon
(unpublished), 1933.

AND THE VILLAIN STILL PURSUED HER!

THREE MOVIE "MENACES WHO HAVE CAUGHT THE PUBLIC FANCY

CLARK GABLE

RICARDO CORTEZ

LOWELL SHERMAN

MILTON CANIFF / A BAD BOY WITHOUT A MOUSTACHE

GROUP PICTURE
SHOWING RECEPTION COMMITTEE BROTHER(?) CLARENCE EMEDY MIGHT EXPECT IF HE DECIDED TO ATTEND THE GRAND CHAPTER

1—

From the Columbus *Dispatch*, 1929.

2—

From the *Magazine of Sigma Chi*, 1931.

3—

William Gillette as Sherlock Holmes; from the Columbus *Dispatch*, 1930.

DICKIE DARE. *Side-kick of the World's Heroes.*

Introducing: Terry and the Pirates

Milton Caniff's life-story has been told many times, and to tell it once again would seem like a pointless exercise. Since this volume is the first of a series aimed at reprinting in its entirety Caniff's most significant body of work —"Terry and the Pirates"—, some biographical backtracking seems in order. We shall try to keep it short, however.

Milton Arthur Caniff was born in Hillsboro, Ohio, on February 28, 1907. After graduation from Ohio State University in 1930, and a short try at a theatrical career, he finally opted for the cartooning profession. In 1932 he created a human-interest panel ("The Gay Thirties"), and a kid-adventure strip ("Dickie Dare"), both for A. P. Newsfeatures which eventually attracted the notice of the New York *News Syndicate* editors.

The rest of the story can be found in Caniff's own words, at the beginning of this book.

When Caniff started on his assignment, the adventure-strip was already establishing itself as one of the most exciting and promising developments of the form; and Harold Foster and Alex Raymond had already emerged as two of its foremost exponents. With Foster able to call Africa his own with "Tarzan", and Raymond slowly annexing South-East Asia in the wake of "Jungle Jim", Caniff decided upon China as the setting of *his* strip. As the lead characters he chose the same combination of manly hero and boy companion that had been the feature of "Dickie Dare", of which "Terry and the Pirates" (a title thought of by Colonel Patterson of the *News*) seemed at first

not so much an off-shot as a duplication; not for long, however.

It is easy now to see the defects of the early "Terry"; the drawing style is stiff and mannered, the characters caricatural, the dialogue too strained, the situations too unlikely. From John T. McCutcheon, whose work he greatly admired, and from the strips of the twenties, Caniff had inherited a set of conventions that were now running out of steam. Inadequacy of technique, however, does not detract even now from the fascination of Caniff's early work. There is a distinct flavor, a subtle undercurrent of unknown quality, that set the early "Terry", simple as it may be, apart from the other cartoon-adventure features of the period. What makes it all the more disconcerting is that this unknown quality turns out on analysis, to be none of those things which have come to be strongly associated with Caniff's art: it is neither wit, nor characterization, not even inventiveness; it is simple charm. All creators have their own distinctive signature, the display of a personal quality on which to fall back when inspiration is failing and technique alone can no longer carry the load. With Harold Foster it is majesty, with Alex Raymond brilliance, with Burne Hogarth power. Milton Caniff's most enduring virtue is charm, and this charm was later to prove a strong drawing card in favor of "Terry" when it was pitted against such prestigious features as "Flash Gordon", "Prince Valiant", and "Tarzan".

Be as it may, Caniff was slowly transcending the limitations of his technique. Not long after the end of the first episode (January 19, 1935), stirrings can already be felt. On January 28, enter Normandie Drake. Spoiled, capricious, headstrong, and unmistakeably feminine (in contrast to the cardboard appearance of Caniff's earlier female characters), Normandie will be the first of a long and glamorous cortege of "Caniff girls"; the first sign of Caniff's artistic sophistication.

Along with characterization, the plotting improves also, both in content and in treatment, although there can hardly be said that it foreshadows a breakthrough in story-telling. The most promising changes are stylistic. "Terry" is slowly coming to life, emerging from the stiffness and rigidity of its beginnings, and evolving towards a freer, more fluid style of visual narration. As early as March of 1935, this mutation is becoming obvious, as Milton Caniff's sense of pacing and showmanship blend with Noel Sickles' functional draftmanship and superior technique. A panel such as the second one of the May 13 strip is typical Caniff already in its neatness and understatement. It stands as a significant, if isolated, landmark in Caniff's progression from fastidious formlessness to formal excellence.

This first (or "primitive") period of "Terry and the Pirates" may be said to have ended somewhere between March and June of 1935. It is easy in retrospect to discover in these early drawings intimations of greatness. And traces of Caniff's outstanding artistic qualities are already there, of course. Spontaneous generation is as foreign to art as to science. But the chief interest of these strips lies in their historical value. Very simply they mark the debut of an important artist (his previous efforts are of little significance). Moreover, and to the best of my knowledge, these "Terry" episodes have never been reprinted in their integrality, and while Caniff's later achievements may tower over these modest beginnings, none can equal their fragile and nostalgic virtue.

The third episode of "Terry" reproduces the daily strips originally published from August 18, through December 18, 1935. In many ways this is "Terry's" most interesting period, as we witness, almost day by day, the maturation of Milton Caniff's talent and the evolving of his unique style.

As the story-line becomes more and more complex, and the action less and less juvenile, Caniff's universe expands and assumes shape. Villains and supporting characters acquire density and verissimilitude, while the Chinese locale comes more sharply into focus. By the end of 1935, Terry has lost his primitive "cartoony" face, and is taking on the features of the bright, rather good-looking young boy he has become. Along with the strip, he is entering adolescence.

By now it had become apparent that a great deal of influences were working on Caniff who was trying his best to blend them into some coherent whole. Some of these influences were literary —reminiscences of Somerset Maugham and Rudyard Kipling—, some didactic — readings from text-books on the Far East and China—, but none was as decisive as the pioneering work done at the time by Noel Sickles.

Caniff and Sickles had known each other since their childhood days in Dayton, Ohio. Both embarked on a cartooning career, both started at Associated Press Newsfeatures, and to stretch the similarity even further they both shared a common studio. By the end of 1934, while Caniff was toiling on "Terry", Sickles had taken over "Scorchy Smith" from John Terry, and had evolved a comic-strip style of his own, based on the use of brush-drawing in order to achieve quasi-impressionistic atmospheric effects and a startlingly visual delineation of action. In view of the two men's long-standing friendship and close relationship, constant interchange between Sickles' brilliant draftsmanship and Caniff's dramatic talent became inevitable. (It is to Caniff's credit that he never tried to downgrade Sickles' contribution, as is evidenced in his preface, as well as in other writings).

By 1935 the two men were working closely together. At times, Sickles would pencil a whole sequence of "Terry" while Caniff busied himself with the continuity for "Scorchy Smith". (In addition they were collaborating, under the pen-name of Paul Arthur, on the Mr. Coffee Nerves advertising strip for Postum). It is therefore not altogether surprising to see some of Sickles' best work crop up in "Terry and the Pirates".

But Caniff was fast outgrowing Sickles, and he now endeavored to familiarize himself with the achievements of other cartoonists, notably Roy Crane's, working them into his own scheme of things; in a way Caniff used Sickles' style as a shell into which he poured substance. Where Sickles showed a flair for visual effect, Caniff was to add a fine dramatic sense; where Sickles used his black and white contrasts to endow a scene with atmosphere. Caniff used them to suffuse the action with a subtle, all-pervasive mood. There is between Sickles and Caniff the same difference as exists between assonance and harmony, shape and form. Sickles was a better craftsman. His detractors to the contrary, Caniff is a greater artist.

By the end of 1935, Caniff was already carrying on a synthesis of contradictory forms, a fusion, however improbable, of the futile and the relevant, the far-fetched and the immediate. A painstaking attention to details, in which the tracing of the balloons and the lettering (done by Frank Engli) received as much attention as the arrangement of characters, a faithful recreation of place and setting, all combined to transcend the fantasies of the plot into an obsessive picture of China — a China that had been as unknown to its creator as to his readers. Here is how Caniff recalls this incredible feat:

"I have never been to China, so I go to the next best place, the Public Library. From its picture file, and with careful clipping of every scrap of data on things Oriental, combined with a dash of *Encyclopedia Brittancia,* I am able to piece together a pretty fair background of Far Eastern lore. For authentic speech mannerisms I plow through a pile of books by traveled people from Pearl Buck to Noel Coward. By now I am an arm-chair Marco Polo and tipping my hat to every Chinese laundryman in New York."

Through Crane, through Sickles, Caniff had become aware of the enormous possibilities that cinematic narration brought to the comic-strip. Now he very consciously set out to adapt camera techniques to his own style of story-telling. First through careful framing, elaborate lighting effects, and skillful manipulation of space, he could create a mood that would either underscore the action, or comment (sometimes ironically) on it, or carry the plot forward without recourse to formal dialogue. Fine examples of this technique can be found in the last panel of the September 28 strip (the feeling here is of alienation), the last panel of the October 1st strip (menace), the last panel of the December 19 strip (despondency).

On this panel we close this first volume of "Terry". Caniff is already in possession of the most important elements of his vocabulary, and is evolving his own vital and dynamic syntax. Slowly the different pieces are falling into place. By now Milton Caniff is ready to make a personal statement of style and purpose.

Maurice Horn

First Episode:
The Lost Gold Mine

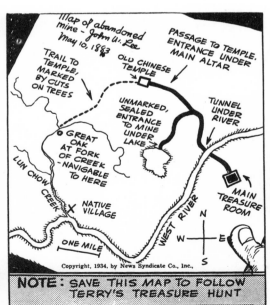

TERRY, PAT AND DALE, HIDDEN BEHIND THE ALTAR GOD IN THE OLD CHINESE TEMPLE WATCH POPPY JOE AND HIS MEN AS THEY SEARCH FOR WHAT THEY THOUGHT WOULD BE THE DEAD BODIES OF THE AMERICANS...

THE FOREIGN DEVILS COULD NOT HAVE VANISHED INTO THIN AIR!

THEY'RE BOUND TO FIND US!— WHEN THEY DO — LET 'EM HAVE IT!

AT THIS MOMENT THE STRANGE CREATURE, WHO HAS WATCHED THE SCENE FROM THE EYE OF THE GREAT STATUE, PLACES A BLOW GUN TO HIS LIPS — THERE IS A SOFT THUD — AND ONE OF THE BANDITS FALLS WITH A DART IN HIS THROAT!

Copyright, 1934, by News Syndicate Co., Inc.

OW!

MILTON CANIFF

12-3

FER PETE'S SAKE!— ONE O' TH' CHINKS HAS BEEN HIT BY AN ARROW —OR SUMTHIN'!

ANOTHER SOFT THUD — AND A SECOND BANDIT FALLS WITH A DART IN HIS NECK

THE AMERICANS! — BEHIND THE IDOL! — GET THE DOGS!

QUICK, PAT! — THEY'VE SEEN US!— THEY THINK WE SHOT THE ARROWS!

STAY UNDER COVER, DALE! — OKAY, TERRY! — GIVE 'EM THE WORKS!

12-4

ight, 1934, by News Syndicate Co., Inc.

MILTON CANIFF

DISCOVERED BY POPPY JOE, TERRY AND PAT EMPTY THEIR GUNS AT THE BANDITS—THEN FIGHT IT OUT—HAND TO HAND!!

12-5 Copyright, 1934, by News Syndicate Co., Inc.,

SO! YAH GOTTA KNIFE, EH?—WELL, I CAN PLAY ROUGH, TOO!

COME! —I CUT OUT THE MELICAN TONGUE!

NOT WHILE I STILL REMEMBER HOW TO TAKE OUT THE SAFETY MAN!

MILTON CANIFF,

COME ON, YOU RICE BURNER!—I CAN LICK YOU IN SPITE OF YOU BEIN' TWICE MY SIZE! —I'M JIST STARTIN'!

12-6

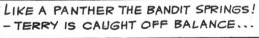

LIKE A PANTHER THE BANDIT SPRINGS! —TERRY IS CAUGHT OFF BALANCE...

Copyright, 1934, by News Syndicate Co., Inc.,

BUT, AS THE GLEAMING KNIFE COMES DOWN— THE FACE APPEARS AGAIN IN THE EYE OF THE STATUE!—A DART SPEEDS ON ITS WAY..

AND THE ORIENTAL SINKS SLOWLY TO THE FLOOR......

MILTON CANIFF,

TERRY AND HIS FRIENDS HAVE REACHED THE TREASURE ROOM THEY FOUGHT SO HARD TO LOCATE - ONLY TO BE CUT OFF FROM ESCAPE BY THE BANDIT CHIEF AND ONE OF HIS MEN...

1-14

YOU ARE SUCH CHARMING GUESTS I WILL KEEP YOU HERE PERMANENTLY! - ALL OF YOU! - STEP INTO THE CORRIDOR! - I WILL SHOW YOU YOUR RESTING PLACE!

YOU MEAN - BURY US ALIVE?

ONLY ONE CONSOLEMENT! - JUS' WAIT 'TIL CONNIE IS GHOST - BOY WILL YOU GET HAUNTED!

Copyright, 1935, by Chicago Tribune-N. Y. News Syndicate Inc.

LISTEN, YOU OLD PUTTY PAN! - MY GRANDFATHER FOUND THIS MINE AND IT BELONGS TO ME! - THE CHINESE GOVERNMENT WILL BACK UP MY CLAIM!

AH, MY FOOLISH ONE - BUT I AM THE GOVERNMENT HERE! - AND I NEED YOUR BONES TO SHOW ANY FUTURE INTRUDERS! KIANG! - PREPARE THE EXPLOSIVES!

AYE, SIRE!

MILTON CANIFF

HERDED INTO AN ABANDONED SHAFT OF THE MINE, TERRY, DALE, PAT AND CONNIE WATCH THE BANDITS PREPARE TO EXPLODE A CHARGE WHICH WILL SEAL THE ENTRANCE

LOW BORN ONE! EVIL NAME! WORM OF ALL WORMS! OOOH MUCH HATE!

MAKE YOURSELVES COMFORTABLE! - YOU WILL BE HERE QUITE SOME TIME!

OH, PAT! - CAN'T WE DO SOMETHING?

1-15

HATE! HATE! HATE! DESPISED KIN OF MANY DEVILS!

HE'D SHOOT US DOWN IN A SECOND IF WE MADE A BREAK! - TAKE IT EASY, DALE!

GITTIN' SHOT WOULD BE BETTER THAN THIS!

Copyright, 1935, by Chicago Tribune-N. Y. News Syndicate Inc.

THE BANDIT LEADER SUDDENLY STIFFENS AS HE FEELS THE HARD MUZZLE OF AN AUTOMATIC PRESSED INTO HIS BACK!

STOW THEM SHENANIGANS, YE FRESHWATER BRIGAND! - DROP THE ARTILLERY BEFORE I LOSES ME POISE AN' SENDS YE T' DAVEY JONES WITH TH' REST O' TH' DERELICTS!

RUN FER IT, YOU YOUNGUNS, WHILE OL POP SETTLES TH' HASH O' THESE TWO SWABS! - HEAD FER TH' TUNNEL UNDER TH' LAKE - I GOT BUSINESS HERE!

MILTON CANIFF

Second Episode:
On a Mystery Cruise

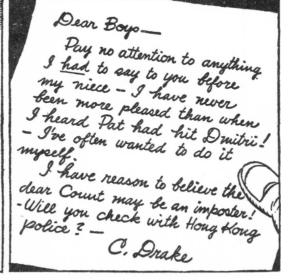

WEAZEL'S COOK HAS COMPLETELY DISAPPEARED..

RUSHING TO THE SPRING TOWARD WHICH THE CHINESE HAD GONE FOR WATER, WEAZEL AND HIS CREW SEE ONLY A HUGE FOOT PRINT IN THE MUD...

4-8

THAT COOK FADED OUT WITHOUT EVEN A YELL!

HE HAD A GUN TOO— THE THING THAT MADE THIS TRACK MUST HAVE BEEN LYING IN WAIT!

IT'S TH' SAME TRACK WE SEEN ON TH' BEACH, WEAZEL!—BLIGH'ME I AIN'T NO LILY BOY, BUT THIS THING'S GOT ME SHAKIN'!

IT'S THE UNKNOWN THAT GETS YOU— IF THEY WOULD ONLY COME OUT IN THE OPEN

MILTON CANIFF

Reg. U S Pat. Off.: Copyright, 1935, by Chicago Tribune-N. Y. News Syndicate, Inc.

WELL, THE COOKS GONE AN' THAT'S THAT— WE'VE GOT TO HAVE WATER ANYHOW— LIMEY, GET A BUCKET AND TAKE SOME TO CAMP...

HEY! THIS SPRING WUZ CLEAR BEFORE— NOW THE WATER IS A SLIMY GREEN! POISON

SLIMY GREEN WATER— WHEN THEY SNATCHED THE COOK THEY MUST HAVE POISONED THE SPRING AT THE SAME TIME!

LOOK AT THAT STUFF!—ONE SWIG OF IT AND YOU'D KEEL OVER IN A SECOND! WEAZEL—THIS 'ERE'S A BLOOMIN' MESS!

4-9

SO FAR SO GOOD!—HOW'RE THEY TAKIN' IT, PAT?

HOOK LINE AND SINKER— IF THAT CAN OF SOUP JUST HOLDS OUT WE'LL HAVE 'EM CRAZY WITH THIRST BEFORE LONG!

MILTON CANIFF

THE SUPPLIES TERRY AND PAT FOUND ON THE WRECKED YACHT ARE SERVING THEM WELL— FOR THE "POISONED WATER" IS NOTHING BUT WELL DILUTED PEA SOUP.. —BUT WEAZEL AND HIS MEN DARE NOT TASTE THE UNSAVORY BREW...

CANNIBALS OR NO CANNIBALS WE'VE GOT TO HAVE WATER! GO FIND ANOTHER SPRING!

BUT THERE AIN'T NO OTHER SPRING AROUND 'ERE— WE LOOKED WHEN WE FIRST LANDED— AND BESIDES — I AIN'T AIMIN' TO MAKE A BANQUET FER A LOT O' 'OWLIN' 'EATHENS!

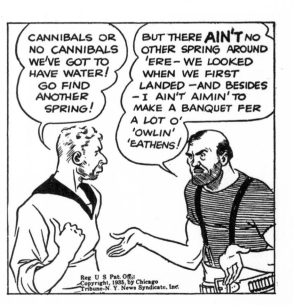

Reg U S Pat. Off.: Copyright, 1935, by Chicago Tribune-N. Y. News Syndicate, Inc.

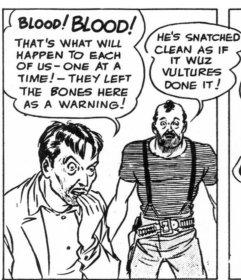

LIMEY AND THE COUNT HAVE OPENLY REBELLED AGAINST WEAZEL'S LEADERSHIP — AND NORMANDIE LOSES NO TIME TELLING WEAZEL THAT HIS TWO CONFEDERATES ARE PLOTTING TO TURN ON HIM....

4-17

TH' DIRTY RATS! SO THEY THINK THEY CAN BUMP ME OFF AND COLLECT ALL THE RANSOM DOUGH THEMSELVES!

WAIT! DON'T DO ANYTHING FOOLISH, MR. WEAZEL!

THEY'RE TWO AGAINST ONE! — IF ANYTHING HAPPENS TO YOU I DON'T KNOW **WHAT** I'LL DO!

YEAH! I'D BETTER COOK UP SOME EXCUSE TO GET THEIR GUNS FIRST! — THANKS!

LATER IN THE DAY WHILE WEAZEL IS TAKING HIS TURN ON WATCH IN THE BLAZING HEAT — NORMANDIE MANAGES TO GET THE OTHER TWO ALONE...

SHHH! — SPEAK IN WHISPERS! WEAZEL IS PLOTTING TO GET YOUR GUNS SO HE CAN TAKE ME HOME AND COLLECT ALL THE RANSOM MONEY — I THINK HE TAMPERED WITH THE BOAT MOTOR DELIBERATELY! — I'M **SO** AFRAID!

WOT?

GIVE ME YOUR GUNS — WE'LL KEEP 'EM IN A CENTRAL STACK SO WE CAN GET AT 'EM EASY IN CASE OF AN ATTACK!

SO THAT'S YER GAME!

4-18

NO, NO! — DON'T DO IT, LIMEY! — HE WANTS TO KILL US! — WE KNOW TOO MUCH!

TAKE IT EASY, COUNT! — NOW LOOKIT 'ERE, WEAZEL — YOU KNOW THAT AIN'T SENSIBLE!

I KNOW WHAT YOU TWO RATS ARE UP TO — — IF YOU THINK YOU CAN RUB ME OUT AND COLLECT THE RANSOM DOUGH YERSELVES, — YER CRAZY!

'EY, WAIT!

FERGIT THAT RANSOM TALK! WE GOTTA WORRY ABOUT SAVIN' OUR 'IDES FROM THEM BLOODY CANNIBALS!

FIGHT, YOU DOGS! — I DON'T THINK IT WILL BE VERY LONG NOW!

DON'T TRY TO SOFT SOAP ME!

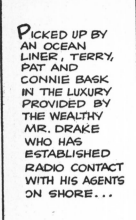

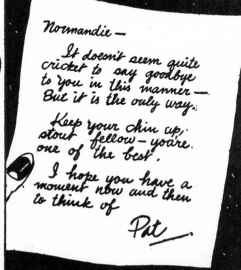

USHERED INTO THE PRISON OFFICE TO MEET THEIR ACCUSER, TERRY PAT AND CONNIE ARE AMAZED TO FIND NORMANDIE DRAKE WAITING FOR THEM....

7-1 Reg. U. S. Pat. Off.: Copyright, 1935, by Chicago Tribune-N. Y. News Syndicate, Inc.

WELL, BOYS— YOU DON'T SEEM VERY HAPPY TO SEE ME — AND YOU REALLY SHOULD, YOU KNOW!

IF YOU'RE NOT TOO BUSY LAUGHING AT US —WOULD YOU MIND, EXPLAINING WHAT THIS IS ALL ABOUT?

OF COURSE ..WHEN I WASN'T ABLE TO FIND YOU IN SINGAPORE I REMEMBERED THE TEN THOUSAND DOLLAR CHECK MY UNCLE GAVE CONNIE...

MILTON CANIFF

...KNOWING, THAT TO CASH SUCH A LARGE CHECK YOU'D GO TO THE BANK IT WAS DRAWN ON, I RADIOED THEM TO HOLD YOU AS FORGERS. I SIGNED THE MESSAGE "DRAKE" WHICH IS, AFTER ALL, MY NAME !.. AND THAT, CHILDREN, IS HOW AUNTIE NORMANDIE CAUGHT UP WITH THE THREE LIL' RUNAWAY PIGGIES!

WANTED !

I SUPPOSE YOU THINK IT WAS PRETTY SMART TO HAVE THE SINGAPORE POLICE HOLD TERRY, CONNIE AND ME FOR FORGERY !

YES! —FRANKLY, I THINK IT WAS PRETTY DARNED SMART!

7-2

BUT I DON'T UNDERSTAND YOU, NORMANDIE! —WHY ARE YOU FOLLOWING US? WHY SHOULD A GIRL LIKE YOU WANT THE COMPANY OF THREE TRAMPS LIKE US?

THREE OF YOU? —ARE YOU BLIND ?— I'M IN LOVE WITH YOU —NOT TERRY AND CONNIE ! —AS FAR AS I'M CONCERNED THEY DON'T EXIST !

OH GULLYWUMPS! WE IS NUTHIN' BUT SPOOKS —JUS' HAUNTS IN TH' HOOSYGOW!

MILTON CANIFF

Reg. U. S. Pat. Off.: Copyright, 1935, by Chicago Tribune-N. Y. News Syndicate, Inc.

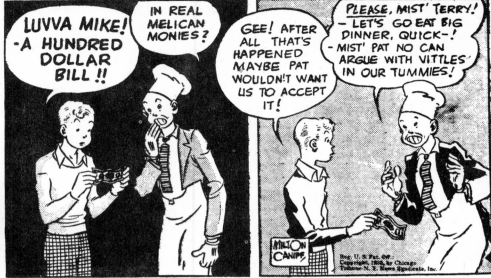

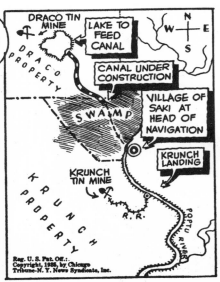

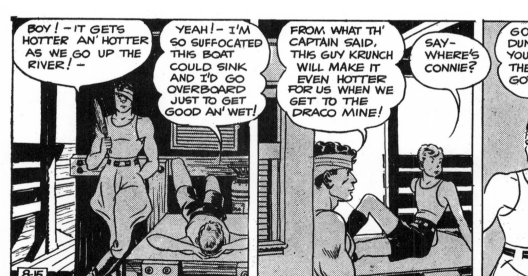

Third Episode:
Thieves and Lovers

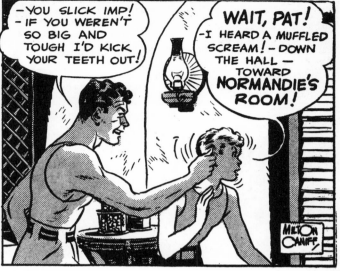

9-16

In their first meeting with Krunch, the boys and Normandie come off with flying colors

— But realizing their advantage is only momentary they leave for the Draco mine at once!

THEY CROSSED TH' RIVER, MR. KRUNCH —THEY'RE HEADIN' FER TH' SPUR TRACK THAT RUNS T' TH' DRACO CAMP!

KLON SU! MAKI! —PUJACK!— YOU KNOW WHAT TO DO! GO!— DON'T FAIL!

SO!

Y'UH'!

MEANWHILE— ACROSS THE RIVER AT THE DRACO LANDING....

WHAT IN THE WORLD IS THIS THING!

IT'S THE NARROW GAUGE THAT CARRIES SUPPLIES TO YOUR UNCLE'S MINE— GET ON!

MILTON CANIFF

WHEE! WE'RE OFF FOR TH' DRACO MINE— AN' OL' KRUNCH IS BITIN' HIS NAILS!

HE'S NO DUMBJOHN TERRY!— WE'LL HEAR FROM HIM!

9-17

THIS AIN'T A BAD RAIL ROAD PAT!— WHY DON'T THEY USE THIS TO CARRY TIN ORE —'STEAD O' BUILDIN' A CANAL?

TOO EXPENSIVE! —WITH A CANAL THEY CAN HAUL MORE STUFF FOR LESS MONEY!

— KRUNCH KNOWS TH' DRACO'S A BETTER MINE—AN' HE'S TRYIN' T' STOP 'EM SO HE'LL HAVE NO COMPETITION IN TH' TIN TRADE 'ROUND HERE?

RIGHT! IF THE CANAL GOES THROUGH IT'LL RUIN KRUNCH!

FUNNY BUSINESS—! GUYS GET KILLED SO ONE FIRM CAN SELL MORE DISH PANS THAN THE OTHER!

IS BATTLE OF BUCKETS!— CHINESE PEOPLES NOT SO DUMB LIKE!— YEARS HAVE TAUGHT-IS BETTER TO LAUGH WITH LITTLE THAN TO MOURN WITH MUCH!— AH! PLOVERB!

MILTON CANIFF

WHILE PAT AND A DOUBLE GUARD WAIT IN THE DARK FOR KRUNCH AND HIS MEN TO ATTACK, NORMANDIE DRESSES AND STEPS OUT INTO THE QUIET JUNGLE NIGHT....

9-30

MEANWHILE, AT PAT'S POST NEAR THE EDGE OF THE CLEARING.....

PASS THE WORD ALONG.. FIRST MAN ATTACKED FIRES THREE RAPID SHOTS AS A WARNING SIGNAL...

PAT! PAT!

NORMANDIE! —WHAT'RE YOU DOING HERE?

MILTON CANIFF

Reg. U. S. Pat. Off..
Copyright, 1935, by Chicago Tribune-N. Y. News Syndicate, Inc.

NORMANDIE! YOU SHOULDN'T BE HERE! KRUNCH IS SURE TO ATTACK US TONIGHT!

I COULDN'T SLEEP!—TOO SCARED!—I WANT TO BE NEAR YOU!

10-1

YOU SHOULD BE BACK IN THE CABIN! —THESE WOODS MAY BE FULL OF KRUNCH'S THUGS!

I FEEL SAFER HERE! —IT'S SO QUIET AND SPOOKY TONIGHT!

OKAY—BUT KEEP ALERT —WE'RE IN A SPOT!

MILTON CANIFF

Reg. U. S. Pat. Off..
Copyright, 1935, by Chicago Tribune-N. Y. News Syndicate, Inc.

PAT AND NORMANDIE HAVE DISAPPEARED DURING THE NIGHT..

TERRY REALIZES THAT KRUNCH HAS AT LAST PLAYED A TRUMP CARD — AND THAT IT IS UP TO HIM TO FIND THEM BEFORE THE WILY TRADER HAS A CHANCE TO MAKE HIS NEXT MOVE...

10-7

BUT MIST'PAT AN' MISSY DLAKE GONE!—WHY YOU WANT GIVE SOME SLEEPY NATIVE HAIR CUT!

NEVER MIND, CONNIE—! C'MON INTO THE BUNK HOUSE!

THIS GUY'LL DO! —SNIP OFF HIS LOCKS! — CAREFUL — DON'T WAKE 'IM!

OKESY DANDY —BUT SEEMS FOOLISHY TO ME!

MILTON CANIFF

ALLITE!— GOT HAIR — NO WAKUM MALAY!— WHAT DO NOW TIME?

I'LL GIVE THAT HAIR A SCRUBBIN' —YOU GO TO THE FIRST AID TENT AN' GET A BIG BOTTLE OF IODINE!

Reg. U. S. Pat. Off.:
Copyright, 1935, by Chicago Tribune-N. Y. News Syndicate, Inc.

COMES CONNIE WITH IODINE! BUT MIST' PAT AN' MISSY DLAKE MAYBE IN GLAVE DANGER— WHAT GOOD'LL BROWN WATER DO?

PLENTY!— BRING THESE NATIVE CLOTHES AN' C'MON — WE'RE DUCKIN' THROUGH TH' JUNGLE!

10-8

CONNIE NO KETCHUM! — WHAT FOR ALL SUCH MONKEY DOODLES?

NOW LOOK! —HERE'S MY PLAN...

.. I DIDN'T WANTA TALK AROUND THE CAMP—KRUNCH MAY HAVE SPIES THERE.... KRUNCH MUSTA TAKEN NORMANDIE AN' PAT TO HIS HEADQUARTERS AT HIS MINE... WE'RE GONNA DRESS AS NATIVE BOYS AN' GO TO KRUNCH'S PLACE AN' ASK FOR WORK!

Reg. U. S. Pat. Off.:
Copyright, 1935, by Chicago Tribune-N. Y. News Syndicate, Inc.

YEAH—BUT YOU NO NATIVE BOY— YOU VELLY NICE MELICAN FELLER!

...NOT FOR LONG! —GIVE ME THAT IODINE, AN' TH' HAIR WE SWIPED, —AN' THAT ADHESIVE TAPE — I'M CHANGING MY NATIONALITY!

MILTON CANIFF

TERRY, DISGUISED AS A DEAF AND DUMB MALAY BOY, HAS BEEN TAKEN INTO KRUNCH'S QUARTERS — KRUNCH ROUGHS HIM AROUND A BIT TO SEE IF HE IS FAKING — THEN, WITH TERRY CARRYING THE LIGHT, THEY START THROUGH AN UNDERGROUND PASSAGE....

10-21

Reg. U. S. Pat. Off.,
Copyright; 1935, by Chicago
Tribune-N. Y. News Syndicate, Inc.

HE MUST BE LEADIN' ME TO NORMANDIE AN' PAT! — HE THINKS I'M DEAF AN' DUMB SO HE MUST BE UP TO SOMETHING HE DOESN'T WANT OVERHEARD!

PRESENTLY THE PASSAGE WALLS BECOME DAMP AND MOSSY

OH GOLLY! — WE'RE UNDER WATER-OR CLOSE TO IT!

KRUNCH STOPS, OPENS AN IRON DOOR, AND MOTIONS TERRY TO GO IN....

MAKILYA! — BRING AMERICAN GIRL!

COMES 'MELICAN GAL, MASTER!

OOOH! — THAT LIGHT HURTS MY EYES!

10-22

SO — IT'S THE NOTORIOUS MR. KRUNCH IN PERSON! — I EXPECTED YOU SOONER!

SIT DOWN!

YOUR HOSPITALITY OVERWHELMS ME! SHALL I TAKE THE DIVAN OR THE RED PLUSH ARM CHAIR?

SIT DOWN!

OKAY — YOU'RE HEADMAN RIGHT NOW — BUT I PITY YOU WHEN WE GET OUT OF HERE AND PAT RYAN GETS HIS HANDS ON YOU!

OPTIMIST!

Reg. U. S. Pat. Off.:
Copyright, 1935, by Chicago
Tribune-N. Y. News Syndicate, Inc.

WITH TERRY DISCOVERED AND KNOCKED OUT, KRUNCH PREPARES TO GET NORMANDIE TO SIGN AWAY THE DRACO MINE BY PUTTING PAT IN THE "IRON LADY", A MEDIEVAL TORTURE MACHINE

PUT IT HERE! — I WANT TO EXPLAIN THE IRON LADY TO RYAN AND THE GIRL!

YOU DON'T NEED TO EXPLAIN IT!

YOU KNOW THAT IT IS LINED WITH KNIVES — AND WHEN THE DOOR IS SLOWLY CLOSED THE OCCUPANT IS STABBED IN A HUNDRED PLACES!

OOOH! — I KNOW IT ONLY TOO WELL!

THEN MAYBE YOU'D RATHER SIGN OVER YOUR DRACO MINE TO ME THAN SEE YOUR SWEETHEART PUT IN THE BOX?

YES! YES! — I'LL SIGN ANYTHING!! GIVE ME THE PEN!

AH! — THE IRON LADY IS A GOOD CONVINCER! — SIGN HERE, MISS DRAKE!

NO, NORMANDIE! NO!

THERE! — NOW UNTIE PAT! YOU HAVE MY SHARE OF THE MINE! — LET US GO!

— SO YOU COULD RUN TO THE POLICE? — OH, NO!

— IF YOUR BODIES ARE FOUND IN THE JUNGLE PIERCED BY POISONED NATIVE ARROWS THERE WILL BE NO AWKWARD EXPLANATIONS FOR ME TO MAKE . . . .

AT THIS MOMENT A LONG WAIL ISSUES FROM THE IRON LADY — AND SMOKE POURS FROM THE UGLY MOUTH..

OOOO!

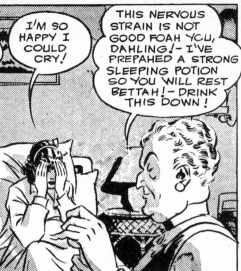

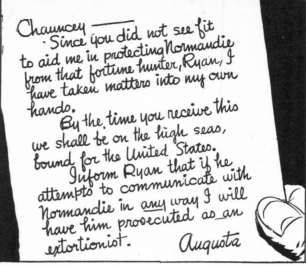